FELIX MENDELSSOHN BARTHOLDY

QUARTET

for 2 Violins, Viola and Violoncello
A minor/a-Moll/La mineur
Op. 13

Ernst Eulenburg Ltd

London · Mainz · Madrid · New York · Paris · Tokyo · Toronto · Zürich

I.	Adagio — Allegro vivace	1
II.	Adagio non lento	16
III.	Intermezzo. Allegretto con moto — Allegro di molto	24
IV.	Presto — Adagio non lento	32

All rights reserved. No part of this publication may be reproduced, stored in a retrieval system, or transmitted in any form or by any means, electronic, mechanical, photocopying, recording or otherwise, without the prior written permission of Ernst Eulenburg Ltd., 48 Great Marlborough Street, London W1V 2BN.

Quartet No. 2

F. Mendelssohn-Bartholdy, op. 13
1809—1847

I

E. E. 1168

Ernst Eulenburg Ltd

Allegro vivace

10

poco piu animato

E.E. 1168

Intermezzo.
Allegretto con moto

III

Allegro di molto

26

E.E. 1168

40

E.E. 1168

E. E. 1168